Kindness from A to Z

Written By Val Pugh-Love

Illustrated By Willie A. Love, II

Printed in the United States of America.

First Printing, 2016

ISBN: 978-0-9982706-0-9

Val Pugh, LLC

Shreveport, LA 71129
www.valpughlove.com

Dedication

Chandler, Chase, Tre, & Kennedy: Keep being kind to each other and yourselves until the end of time.

We are awesome.

1

You are beautiful.

2

This food is delicious.

5

You are my friend.

They are gorgeous.

He is handsome.

8

I Love you.

They are **marvelous** dancers.

13

We are nice.

He is an outstanding swimmer.

15

I am a queen.

She is ravishing.

She is a sweetheart.

19

They are terrific gymnasts.

20

His smile is vibrant.

22

They are wonderful students.

23

Her cake looks yummy.

25

We are zealous.

Made in the USA
Middletown, DE
05 June 2022

66615883R10018